The Manga Jesus
Book Two

Siku — artist, theologian and musician — is one of Britain's leading comic book creators and conceptualists. He has worked for *2000AD*, on stories such as *'Judge Dredd'*, *'Slaine'* and a strip he co-created called *'Pan-African Judges'*. He has also worked for Marvel UK and COM X and has been credited on a number of computer games such as *Evil Genius*. More recently, he has been developing concept work for television commercials and producing freelance work for Nike, Nickelodeon IP, a BBC documentary-drama series and an animated television series.

Siku's works have been published in several books, including *Images 22: The Best of British Illustration* and *Digital Art Masters*. His work is prominent in Dez Skinn's *Comic Art Now* (a compilation of the best of international contemporary comic book art). His television appearances include ITV's *The London Programme*, Channel 4's *The Big Breakfast* and *More 4 News*, Channel 5's *Chris Moyles Show* and BBC One's *Heaven and Earth* show. He has also written editorials for magazines and industry books including *The Art of Game Worlds*.

Siku dreams of flying one day, just like Superman. Until then, he'll make do travelling around on the London Underground.

The Manga Jesus
Book Two

SIKU

H
HODDER

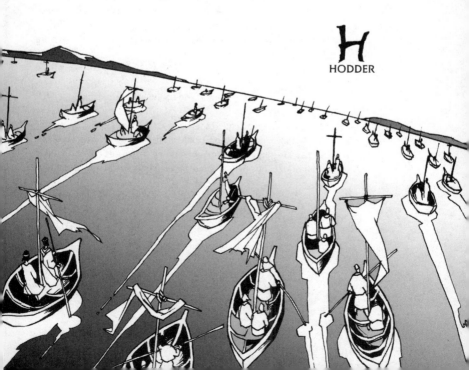

The Manga Jesus: Book Two
Copyright © 2009 by Siku

First published in Great Britain in 2009 by Hodder & Stoughton
An Hachette UK company

1

A CIP catalogue record for this title is available from the British Library

ISBN 978 0 340 96406 4

Printed and bound in Italy by Legoprint S.P.A.

Hodder & Stoughton policy is to use papers that are natural, renewable
and recyclable products and made from wood grown in sustainable
forests. The logging and manufacturing processes are expected to
conform to the environmental regulations of the country of origin.

Hodder & Stoughton Ltd
338 Euston Road
London NW1 3BH

www.hodderfaith.com

ACKNOWLEDGEMENTS

As I concluded the first book in this series, my editor David Moloney moved on and joined the clan of freelancers like myself. I am indebted to him for his confidence in my ability to perform, and from time to time, the risks he took on my behalf.

As he leaves, I get a brand spanking new editor, boxed, bows an' all. When I opened the lid, surprise, surprise, it was Mr Ian Metcalfe. We met a couple of years ago as he backed some other project of mine. Thanks for making sure my spelling didn't 'show me up'! Those *proof marks*...the last time I saw them so formal was back in school studying graphic design. That was...yonks ago!

Again, props to Dr Gempf of the London School of Theology. That answering message of yours...nuts!

The Edge Group.

The baby Tali, the way you giggled half asleep at 2:00am when you realised Daddy was home.

Here we go again...

Ding ding ding! Jesus... fiction... comic book... superhero. Alarm bells!

I'm a historian. My PhD thesis compared the work of St Luke with the best of the Greek and Roman historians. This project flashed twenty different kinds of red lights in my head.

OK, I knew Siku. He did an undergraduate degree in theology where I work, The London School of Theology, formerly known as London Bible College. He's a great student. I worked with him on the New Testament portion of The Manga Bible, which illustrates the text of Scripture in manga form. It is most excellent.

But this?! To fill in gaps that the Bible leaves blank?
To employ a medium we associate with ludicrous and outrageous fantasies to portray what I think is truth? Ding ding ding!

I was approached to be the 'theological consultant'. Ummm. Thought I'd have to say no. Decline gracefully. This might be going too far.

Then I saw the material. Whoa! He's done his homework! He knows the ancient sources; he's sensitive to the ancient culture. Whoa!

Then I saw the drawings. Wow! He's totally captured John the Baptist; his gap-filling is helpful rather than distracting. And, I'm sorry, for me that IS the Temple.

And then, beyond wow! This is not only filled with learning about the ancient world. It's also so clearly filled with sympathy for the characters and, better still, filled with love for the Scriptures and for the Lord.

You look at these pages — or through these pages — a man pushes the hood back from his head and turns to you. A wry smile. And with the suggestion of a twinkle in his eye, he says to you — to you — 'Oh. By the way… They call me Yeshua — Jesus.'

Gulp.

Yeah, ok, maybe manga comics seemed inappropriate. A worldly medium. An earthen vessel. Just like any of us.

No more alarms; sound the 'all clear'. For some people in today's culture — all very, very clear.

Dr Conrad Gempf, London School of Theology

A KIND OF TARDIS

Eventually, after months of studying various reconstruction maps of 1st century Jerusalem, I came to know the Holy City better than the town where I live in Essex. I have seen Google Earth satellite photographs of my neighbourhood, yet I really can't tell if the local tube station lies either east or west from my home. It's only a seven minute walk from my house, but I simply don't know! Nor can I tell in what direction the local cinema is from where I write this essay at my desk in my living room. But after studying those maps of ancient Jerusalem for several months, my sense of direction *there* works just fine. From Herod's magnificent palace on the west side of the walled capital, adjoining the marketplace in the rich districts called the Agora or Upper City, to the ancient City of David (also called 'the Ophel') on the eastern side. Right next to David's walled city to the left is Herod's magnificent hippodrome. These two parts of Jerusalem are walled. If you read *The Manga Jesus Book One*, you'd remember John's challenge to Antipas. In Chapter Three, the camera pans across the Tyropoean valley towards Herod's hippodrome. The valley which divides these two districts is poorer (Lower City) and not nearly as well planned as the two other districts. In *TMJ1*, John 'the Voice' makes his second challenge at Herod's theatre. This adjoins the wall that borders Upper City. Upper City is millionaire row, Beverly Hills 90210, Platinum Triangle, Bel-Air – 1st century style. Swimming pools, cut-stone palatial homes complete with terracotta roof tiling. Every house is symmetrically arranged on straight roads. You'll find yourselves rubbing shoulders with the rich, the obscenely rich and famous. The High Priest is a local and the legend King David's tomb lies south of the district. Forget what you saw in those Jesus movies of ancient Jerusalem. This is no dust bowl! It is lush and greeeen.

The next day, John 'the Voice', decides to challenge Herod Antipas at the Upper City market place. Again, you are forgiven for thinking this to be yet another mud-fest with shanty kiosks and makeshift stands. No! This place was purpose built. After all, it's the Agora, Bond Street or Rodeo Drive. If you were Peter Parker, and climbed to the roof of this two storey American-style-super-mall, you'd see Herod's towering Roman-style coliseum about three blocks away. Nah, this Jerusalem is no backwater country... no sir!

Well, let's imagine we are making our way toward the Temple to worship. Oh, the Temple... on a clear day, you can see her from miles away. It's just like seeing Wembley Stadium's shimmering metal frame and arc from my publisher's high-rise offices at Euston in London on a sunny clear day, but better! She lies at the highest point of Jerusalem. Apparently, Herod the Great modified the terrain of the Jerusalem mount and valley just to make sure he could fit the entire thing on the mount. We can make our way to the south-west side of the Temple. That way, we get to avoid the Lower City. You see, it's not like walking along Broadway in New York and then suddenly finding yourself in a rough neighbourhood. No ma'am. Here, you don't get into the poor districts 'by accident'. But then, if you decided to go through Lower City, you'd walk the paved main course of the Tyropoean valley. You'd get a clearer view of the Temple; bathed in sunlight, her white stones dazzle. The façade of the Sanctuary is plated with gold and with white stone... probably marble. It blinds the eyes as sun rays flicker off the gold spikes on the roof tops. You'd walk past the pool of Siloam where Jesus healed a man who was born blind (John 9) and you'd meet Herod's hippodrome racecourse just to the south. To the east of the Temple, across the valley, lies the Mount of Olives – the market place called The Chanuth. From there, you can see the entire building of the Temple.

The entrance of the Temple is south-side. There are three doors on the far right (triple Huldah gates) and two doors to the far left side (double Huldah gates). You enter through the right side doors and leave through the left side doors after going through the purification rite. The triple doorway leads you through an elaborately decorated tunnel-type stairway that goes directly upwards to the courts. The court is massive! The entire complex is approximately the size of thirty-five football fields! Considering that this building is famous throughout the Roman Empire for its size (it's probably the largest religious building in the known world) and sheer beauty; considering that this building is the centre of Jewish political and spiritual life, why don't we get to see her in those Jesus movies? It's like watching a film where Columbo goes to London, but we don't get to see Big Ben! Yes, I think I got to know my way around ancient Jerusalem better than Essex, and if you read *TMJ1*, you'll know I'm big on the Temple. The next time you visit 1st century Jerusalem, visit that temple.

As we enter the main courts – called Court of the Gentiles (because it was open to all, Jew or non-Jew) – we are stunned by the scale of the open space. Surrounded by porticos with pillars, the entire space would have been used for religious activities: Torah academies for students from all over the country (it was in one of those Torah academy porticos that the twelve year old Jesus was found by his parents, Mary and Joseph); intellectual discussions and lectures as well as witnessing, prayer and debates. It must have been quite a spiritual experience doing all that against the backdrop of such a wonder of a building. Now you see (partly) why Jesus drove the Temple merchants out with such vigour.

Jesus would have healed the sick in this court and he had several debates with his detractors here. Some criticised the Jesus I presented in *The Manga Bible* as trash-talking. Well, wait until you meet the Jesus in *TMJ2*. Towards the end of this book, you'll see the master in fine form – in a manner some will find quite uncomfortable – as he literally chews out his antagonists. But, this is not trash-talking. These debates were how Rabbis proved they were the real deal, not unlike how hip-hop emcees prove themselves in public today. The crowds responded just like crowds responding to a rap battle, and as we approach the climax of *TMJ2*, Jesus raises his game as his opponents throw in everything, including the kitchen sink! For him, it was a fight for the very souls of his audience... no wimps allowed!

The main entrance, as I stated before, is to the south. If you keep walking northwards (like walking toward heaven), you'll see the

Sanctuary. It has two courts: one smaller, inner court inside the larger, outer court. The outer court is called the Court of Women because it is open to female as well as male Jews. Here, Jesus made his final stand against the authorities. They were fatally wounded in three sets of hostile arguments. The master exposed their hypocrisy. It is here that he sees the destitute widow drop her last penny into the collection box in one of several booths surrounding the area. Ironic, that in this Court of Women, the Pharisaic Order, that kept women at bay, was itself exposed for its hypocrisy – by a woman.

The word Pharisee is now a byword for hypocrisy, and Jesus' devastating last stand here is partly the reason why we have come to this understanding of the Pharisees. But, the Pharisees had a lot more in common with Jesus than any other Order. Not all Pharisees were hypocritical or sanctimonious. Their theology was largely correct, but too many of them emphasised ceremonial law over the essence of the Law. For Jesus, this was a no-no. He attacks the entire establishment that kept the people in bondage and perpetuated injustice. Consider, for example, the lifestyle of the priests against that of the people – the priests had the right to consume much of what the people presented in sacrifice. This meant they would eat more meat in two weeks than the general population could eat in a year. Hence the priests, unlike their parishioners, were physically stout and well rounded. The authorities simply lorded themselves over the people, and the people were leaderless. Tax collectors were collaborators and corrupt. A farmer with his harvest would be stopped at toll points and an assessment would be made as to how much was owed to the Empire – at the sole discretion of the collector. You think the IRS has too much power – wait till you meet the tax collectors of the Roman Empire! The Empire simply set a tax target; the tax collectors would bid for the franchise. Whatever excess was collected became profit for the collector. As you can imagine, the system was riddled with corruption and the people were crippled with high taxes. Herod's poorly paid army didn't do much better either, as they robbed and bullied the local population. John 'the

Voice' talks about this just before his tirade against the theologians and lawyers from Jerusalem in *TMJ1*.

'NUTTER', 'DRUNKARD'!

The Temple, though largely completed, was still being built during the time of Jesus. It provided work for the local economy. No doubt, if Joseph had stayed in his home town of Bethlehem (just a few miles from Jerusalem), he could have done a lot of trade there. You would notice from *TMJ1* that he opts for Galilee up north. This is where the master would eventually spend much of his life, learning two trades, as an artisan and rabbi. He would have learnt his trade from his artisan father, and like all boys up to the age of five, he would have learnt the Law at the local synagogue on the outskirts of Nazareth. After the age of five, education became less formal, but it is said that almost everyone in the land of Israel would have been literate.

After the age of five, some went on to further study. For every 1000 students who studied the Bible, only one would make it to rabbi. Jesus was obviously prodigious, and he had the intelligence required to become rabbi. Meanwhile, his more famous (at that time) cousin, John 'the Voice' abandoned his studies for priesthood to become an ascetic prophet. They probably studied together as children during festival breaks and visits. So who was John? He was the hardest kid on the block, that's who he was! He ate locusts for breakfast and wild honey for dessert! He wore clothes made from camel hair held with a leather belt, lived in the desert and attacked the tyrant, Antipas! He was as hard as nails. Some scholars even think Jesus was John's disciple up until he started his ministry. But their paths began to take different turns. One was called a nutter, the other, a drunk! One will begin to decrease, and the other will begin to increase. As they begin the next phase of their story, I arrive back home in 21st century Essex, in my time machine. It's no tardis, but it works just fine, thank you very much.

Siku
From his tardis in Essex, England.
November 2008

SAMARIA.

The Manga Jesus
Chapter 1; The Samaritan woman and the tetrarch's wife.

SIKU

MACHAERUS FORTRESS.
MY LORD ANTIPAS! HEAR MY WORDS! YOU TAKE REFUGE BEHIND THAT WOMAN'S SKIRT, BUT YOU KNOW YOU CANNOT HIDE!
SO YOU HIDE ME INSTEAD. THE WHOLE OF ISRAEL KNOWS THIS!
BUT WHO WILL HIDE YOUR SHAME, ANTIPAS?
ANTIPAS!
ANTIPAS!
UUUGGGG
!

5

PREACHER!

I AM THE ONLY ONE STANDING BETWEEN YOU AND THE EXECUTIONER. YOU SHOULD SHOW MORE RESPECT.

YOU WILL HAVE MY RESPECT, TETRARCH, WHEN YOU RULE JUSTLY!

YOU KNOW OUR PEOPLE. ONE NEEDS TO RULE WITH AN IRON FIST. IT'S THE ONLY WAY TO KEEP THE ROMANS AT BAY.

YOU SIR, RULE, ONLY TO SATISFY YOUR OWN AMBITION! YOU HAVE NEVER LOVED THE PEOPLE!

I SURVIVE! WHAT YOU CALL RUTHLESS **AMBITION,** I CALL SHEER **SURVIVAL.**

I AM THE LAST OF MY FATHER'S CHILDREN. MY BROTHER, **ARCHELAUS,** AND I, BARELY SURVIVED THE POWER STRUGGLE IN MY FAMILY.

YOU KNOW HOW MANY WILLS MY FATHER MADE? SIX! SIX WILLS! SIX WILLS AND TEN WIVES. IF WE SURVIVED, WE SURVIVED BECAUSE WE ARE SURVIVORS, NOT MERELY **AMBITIOUS.** IT'S THE WAY OF THE HERODS.

SOMEBODY PASS ME A BUCKET!

WHAT IS THIS? **PITY-THE-ROYAL SPECIAL?** AM I SUPPOSED TO CRY NOW?

LIFE WAS HARD SO TETRARCH ANTIPAS STOLE HIS HALF-BROTHER'S WIFE! **BOY,** WOULD I LIKE TO SEE WHAT YOUR FAMILY GATHERINGS ARE LIKE!

A FAMILY OF DESPOTS AND INTRIGUE. **BROTHER** PLOTTING AGAINST **BROTHER, FATHER** AGAINST **SONS, MOTHERS** AGAINST **MOTHERS!** YOU ARE AN APPLE THAT FELL QUITE CLOSE TO THE TREE SIR!

Chapter 2
Drunkard!
Nutter!

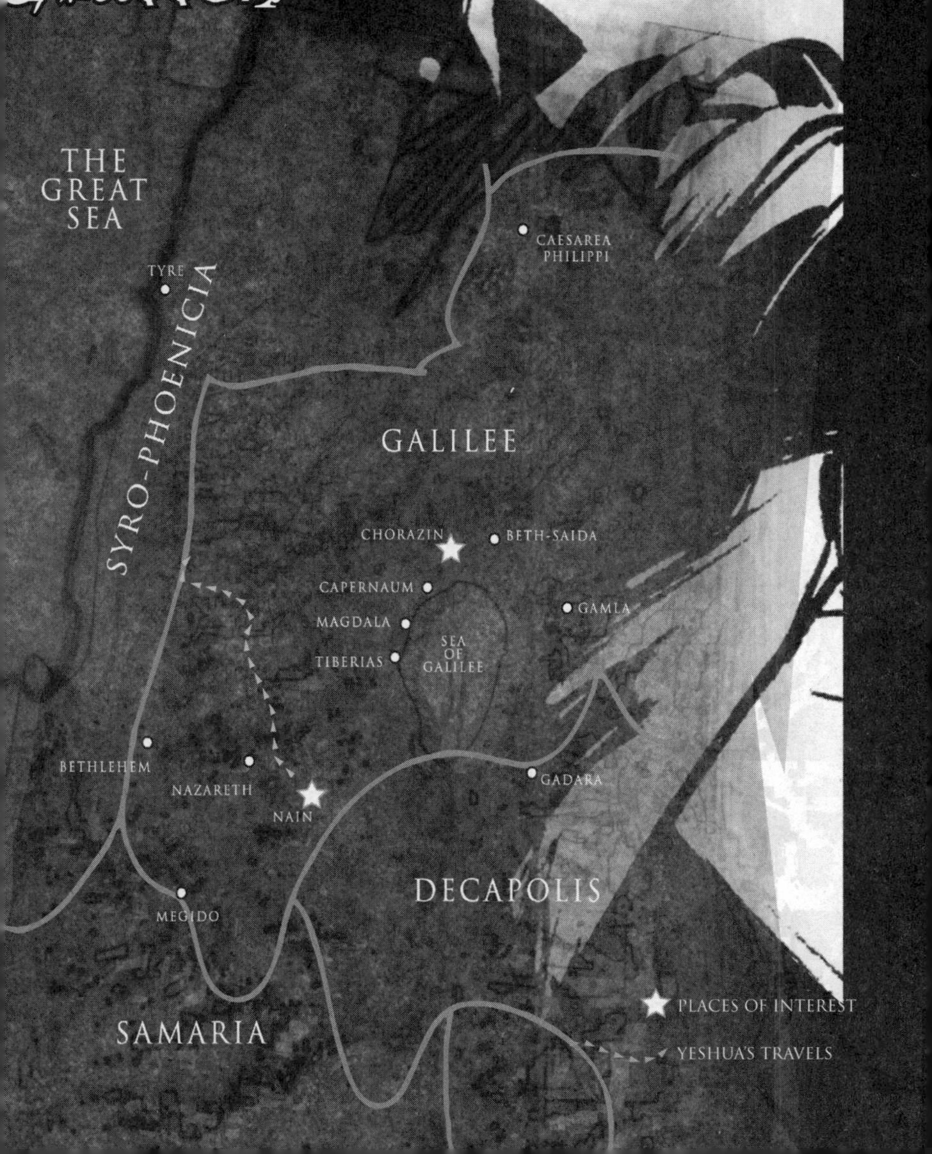

THE
GREAT
SEA

CAESAREA
PHILIPPI

TYRE

SYRO-PHOENICIA

GALILEE

CHORAZIN   BETH-SAIDA

CAPERNAUM

MAGDALA   GAMLA

TIBERIAS   SEA
OF
GALILEE

BETHLEHEM

NAZARETH   GADARA

NAIN

DECAPOLIS

MEGIDO

SAMARIA

PLACES OF INTEREST

YESHUA'S TRAVELS

...LET'S GO MEET OUR AUDIENCE.

WHAT'S UP, ISCARIOT?

SAY, ROCK...

...SINCE I'M NEW TO THE TEAM, WHAT'S THE GOSS ON THE OTHER GUYS?

WELL, THOSE TWO ARE JAMES AND JOHN, THE RABBI CALLS THEM THUNDER BOYZ.

THAT'S MY BROTHER, ANDREW. THE FOUR OF US RUN A FISHING BUSINESS IN CAPERNAUM.

THAT'S PHIL.

NATE. SOMETIMES WE CALL HIM BART.

MATT USED TO BE A TAX MAN.

THOMAS THE TWIN.

KID JAMES.

THADDAEUS.

AND FINALLY THE MYSTERIOUS SIMON. HE USED TO BE A ZEALOT REVOLUTIONARY... WE THINK.

AND YOU, ISCARIOT, WHAT'S YOUR STORY?

ME?... I'M JUST THE BOOK-KEEPER, MATE.

'IN TOTAL, THERE ARE **72** OF US.'

'NOT COUNTING THE CROWDS JOINING US
FROM VILLAGE TO VILLAGE...'

'...TOWN TO TOWN.'

'...CITY TO CITY.'

ON THE GREAT PLAINS OF **ESDRAELON**, 25 MILES SOUTH-WEST OF CAPERNAUM LIES THE TOWN OF **NAIN**.

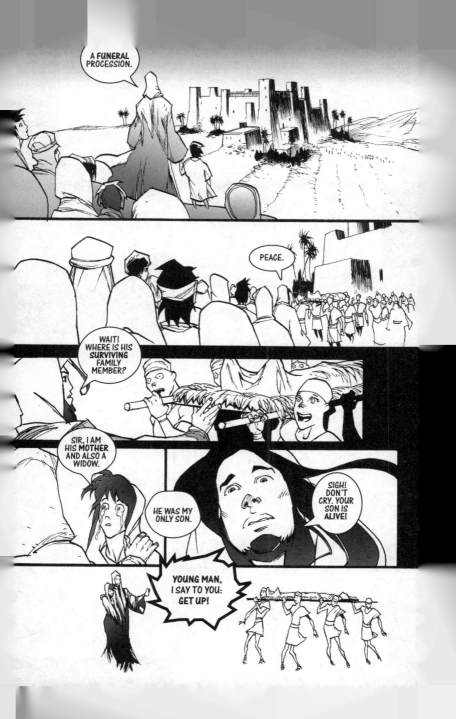

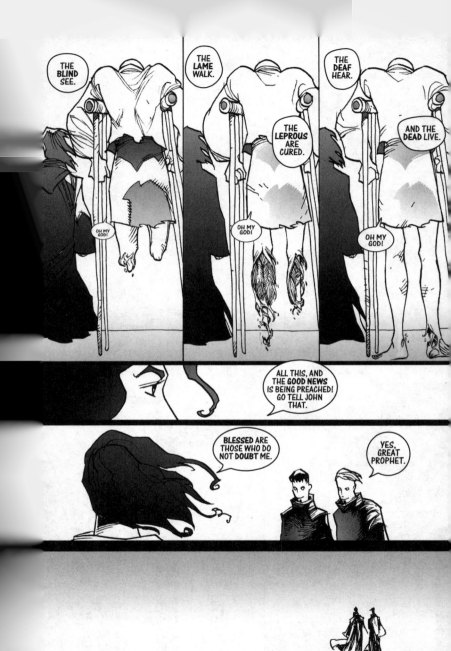

MOMMA!

DID YOU HEAR? LUCCIA WAS CURED.

WHO CURED HER?

ONE OF THE JEWISH SEERS CALLED YESHUA.

DADDY LOVS ME

UUG...

UUGGGH...

AARGGGH!

Chapter 3
Heavy is the crown

THE
GREAT
SEA

CAESAREA
PHILIPPI

TYRE

SYRO-PHOENICIA

GALILEE

CHORAZIN   BETH-SAIDA

CAPERNAUM

MAGDALA   GAMLA

TIBERIAS   SEA
OF
GALILEE

BETHLEHEM

NAZARETH   GADARA

NAIN

DECAPOLIS

MEGIDO

SAMARIA

★ PLACES OF INTEREST

- - ➤ YESHUA'S TRAVELS

TIBERIAS FORTRESS.

PEACE, CHUZA.

PEACE, GUYS. LET'S GO IN THEN.

'IT WAS HEROD ANTIPAS' BIRTHDAY PARTY, A PARTY TO REMEMBER.'

'ALL HIS TOP OFFICIALS WERE PRESENT.'

'THE BEST FOOD, IMPORTED WINE, FAMOUS PERFORMERS.'

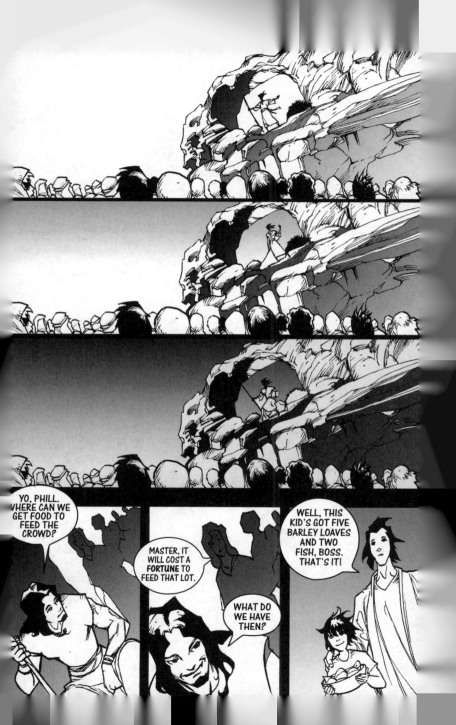

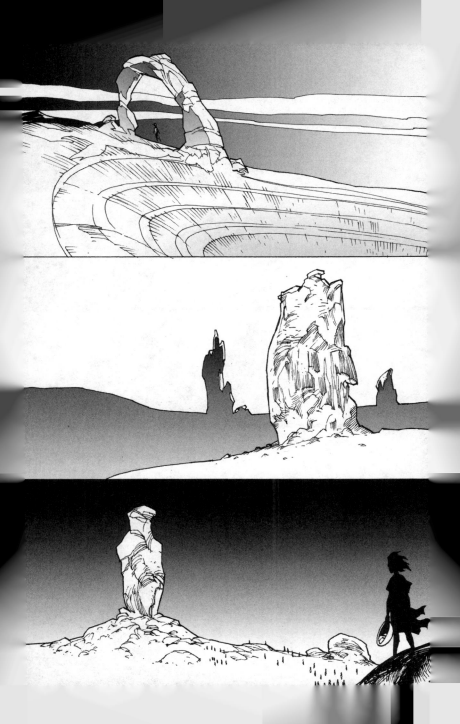

2:55 AM.

WHAT THE
HECK IS
THAT?

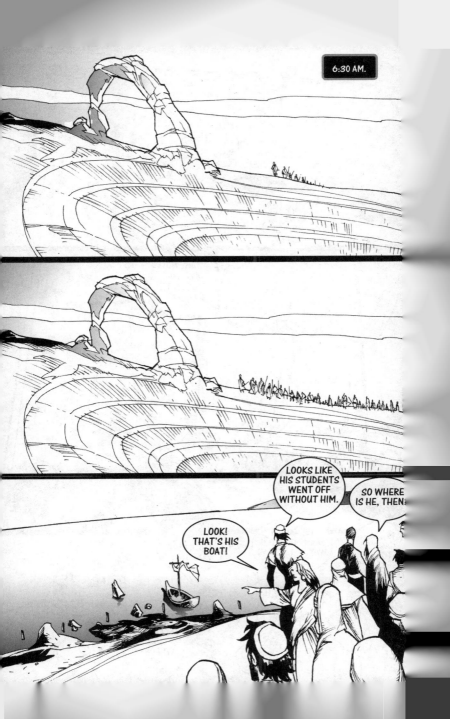

'MASTER, WHY DO THE RABBIS INSIST THAT ELIJAH MUST RETURN FIRST BEFORE THE MESSIAH?'

'ELIJAH DID INDEED RETURN TO SET THINGS IN ORDER, BUT THEY DIDN'T RECOGNISE HIM.'

'LIKE THEIR ANCESTORS, WHO KILLED THE PROPHETS OF OLD, THEY MURDERED HIM.'

'THEY WILL ALSO TREAT ME WITH UTTER CONTEMPT, AND I MUST SUFFER AT THEIR HANDS, AND BE KILLED.'

'O JERUSALEM, JERUSALEM, THE CITY THAT KILLS THE PROPHETS AND STONES GOD'S MESSENGERS!'

'HOW OFTEN I HAVE WANTED TO GATHER YOUR CHILDREN TOGETHER AS A HEN PROTECTS HER CHICKS BENEATH HER WINGS! BUT YOU WOULDN'T LET ME.'

'BUT LOOK! YOUR HOUSE WILL NOW BE EMPTY AND DESOLATE. O JERUSALEM, JERUSALEM, I GRIEVE FOR YOU, O JERUSALEM.'

Chapter 4
Blood on the temple floor!

THE GREAT SEA

TYRE

CAESAREA PHILIPPI

SYRO-PHOENICIA

GALILEE

CHORAZIN   BETH-SAIDA
CAPERNAUM
MAGDALA   GAMLA
TIBERIAS   SEA OF GALILEE

BETHLEHEM

NAZARETH

NAIN

GADARA

MEGIDO   DECAPOLIS

SAMARIA

SHECHEM   SYCHAR
JACOB'S WELL

ARIMATHAEA

PERAEA

EMMAUS   JERICHO

JERUSALEM   BETHANY
BETHLEHEM
HERODIUM

JUDEA

AZA

HEBRON   MACHAERUS

DEAD SEA

ARNON RIVER GORGE

MASADA

BEER-SHEBA

★ PLACES OF INTEREST

◁◁◁ YESHUA'S TRAVELS

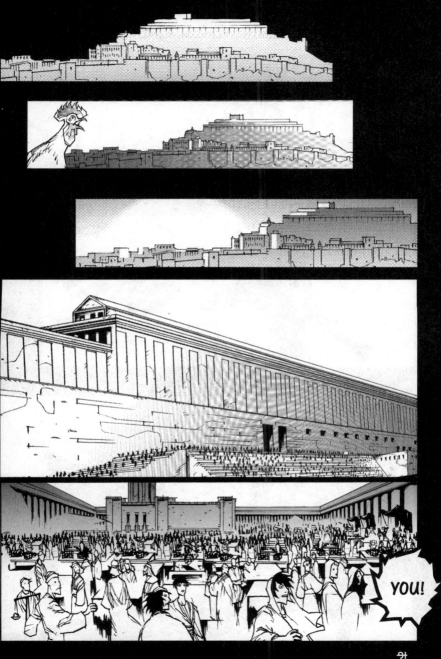

95

LISTEN TO THIS STORY, FOLKS.

'ONCE UPON A TIME, A LANDLORD PLANTED A VINEYARD.'

'HE LEASED IT OUT TO TENANT FARMERS WHILE HE TRAVELLED ABROAD.'

'DURING THE HARVEST, THE LANDLORD SENT SERVANTS TO COLLECT HIS SHARE OF THE CROP.'

'BUT THE TENANTS ATTACKED THEM AND SENT THEM AWAY EMPTY-HANDED.'

'BUT THEY RECEIVED THE SAME TREATMENT.'

'SO THE LANDLORD SENT OTHERS.'

'THEN THE LANDLORD THOUGHT...

...'I KNOW, I'LL SEND MY CHERISHED SON, SURELY THEY'LL RESPECT HIM?''

'WHEN THE TENANTS SAW THE LANDLORD'S SON, THEY DECIDED TO KILL HIM IN ORDER TO INHERIT THE LAND.'

'OF COURSE, THE LANDLORD KILLED THE TENANTS AND LEASED THE VINEYARD TO OTHERS. THE END.'

101

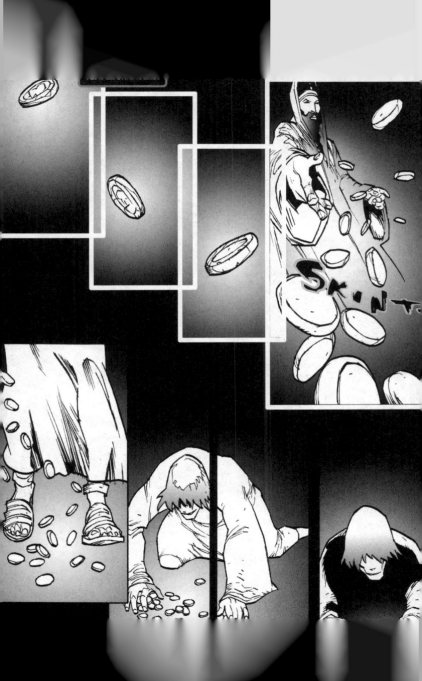

SKETCHES

These next few pages show the development of characters,
storyboards and layouts.

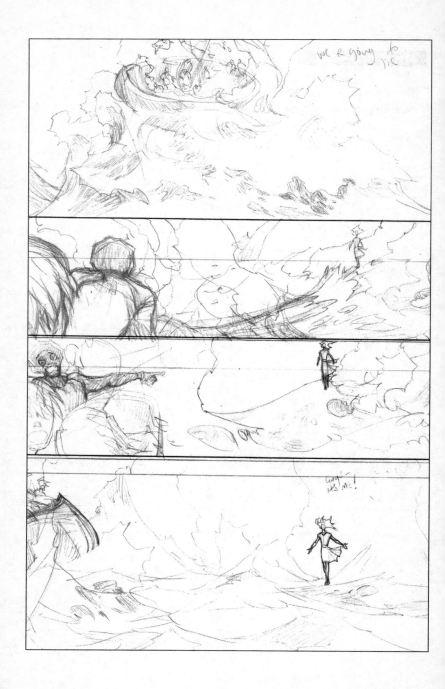

I am the one

Abraham
The father of the Hebrews. Christians claim him as their spiritual father.

Baptism
A purification rite prescribed by Hebrew law, required for certain rites and conversion. John introduced a radical form of baptism which announced impending judgement and the coming kingdom.

Bar Mitzvah
A ritual ceremony marking the 13th year of boyhood, after which the child takes responsibility for their own moral and spiritual conduct and are thereafter considered adults. Today, the similar ceremony for girls is called a Bat Mitzvah.

Caiaphas
High priest and chairman of the Sanhedrin between 18 AD and 37 AD.

Chanuth, the
The market place on the Mount of Olives, across the Kidron valley from the Temple.

Christ, the
From the Greek, literally meaning 'the Anointed'. Its Hebrew origin is 'the Messiah'. In the Old Testament the title implied little more than 'set apart to perform a particular task'.

Contubernia, the
Otherwise called 'the tent group'. Comprising eight legionaries, it was the smallest organised unit in the Roman army.

David, King
Military leader, prophet, musician/ song writer and poet, he was the second king of the united kingdom of Israel. He rose to prominence after killing the Philistine giant warrior Goliath, while he was only a teenager.

Demon possession
When demons lay claim to and reside within a human's body and personality, such is said to be possessed.

Elijah
Considered one of the greatest of the prophets, Elijah lived in the 9th century BC. Jews expect his return as a precursor to the coming of the Messiah.

Ethnarch
A ruler of an ethnic group as designated by Roman power. While this office is higher than the title 'tetrarch', it is not quite as high as the title 'king'. An example of an ethnarch who sought the higher office of king within the Roman Empire was Herod Archelaus, who ruled over Samaria, Judea and Idumea.

Galilee
The largest and furthest north of the three provinces (with Judea and Samaria) that comprised Israel in

Roman times. It also was the most troublesome politically.

Gentiles
Non-Jews and non-followers of the Jewish faith.

Herod
Name used of the kings and rulers in the centuries just before and after Jesus, descended from Herod the Great (and his father Antipater).

Herod the Great
Otherwise known as Herod the Builder, born 73 BC, died 4 BC. Brutal and paranoid client King of Judea and father of Archelaus, Antipas and Philip. He was famous for his many great buildings including the second temple in Jerusalem. His infamous slaughter of the Bethlehem babies and toddlers in his hunt for Yeshua is well known.

Hosanna
It means 'save now' in Hebrew.

Jacob
Grandson of father Abraham, son of Isaac and brother of Esau. His twelve sons were forefathers of the twelve tribes of Israel – they were – Reuben, Simeon, Levi, Judah, Dan, Naphtali, Gad, Asher, Issachar, Zebulun, Joseph and Benjamin.

Jerusalem
The sacred capital of Israel and the Jewish faith. The seat of the Temple of God.

Jews
Descendants of Abraham.

Jeremiah
Jeremiah was one of Israel's greatest prophets. He made use of performance art and props as illustrations of his prophetic warnings to Israel.

Levites
A priestly tribe – descendants of Levi, one of Jacob's sons. As priests, they offered sacrifices, pronounced blessings, provided Temple music, policed the Temple boundaries, blowing trumpets announcing festive occasions, conducted general maintenance of the Temple. They are distinct from the priestly descendants of Aaron.

Maccabees
An epitaph meaning 'the hammer', and the name of a Jewish liberation movement. Inspired by the high priest Mattathias, his sons – Judas Maccabee and his brothers – led a successful revolt against the Seleucid Empire.

Manna
A bread-like food substance miraculously provided by God to the Israelites during their exodus from Egypt. It tasted like wafers made with honey and oil.

Moses
Prophet, priest, liberator, commander-in-chief, political leader, poet, writer, legislator, teacher, miracle worker,

administrator and ethicist. The father of Jewish Law, it is believed he authored the first five books of the Bible. He liberated the Hebrews from Egyptian captivity.

Passover
A Jewish festival celebrating Israel's exodus from slavery in Egypt. It is celebrated in spring time.

Pharisees
An old Jewish sect that promoted a constant state of purity, which they believed would ensure the survival of the nation of Israel. They obeyed both the oral and written law (Torah).

Prophet
An inspired teacher, known at times to predict the future. Sometimes described as a seer.

Rabbi
Literally means 'my great one'. A teacher and master of Jewish religious law. Only the most distinguished students qualify to study to the level of Rabbi.

Sadducees
A priestly, aristocratic caste. They were traditionalists who accepted only the written law as inspired scripture and rejected belief in the afterlife.

Samaritans
Inhabitants of the hill country of Samaria. According to the Mishnah, they were a sect somewhere between Jews and non-Jews. They observed the Law of Moses but rejected all other Jewish traditions. They also rejected worship at the Temple, opting for Mount Gerizim. Their claim, that Samaritan Law was the true religion of ancient Israel was a source of schism.

Sanhedrin
The Jewish high council made up of seventy-one members, both Pharisees and Sadducees. A high priest presided over the council.

Social bandits
Revolutionaries who ravaged the countryside and toll routes. They usually saw themselves as rebels against Roman tyranny and often supported society's poor and outcasts.

Synagogue
Places of worship, religious instruction, education and community in 1st century AD Israel.

Synagogue interpreter (Amora)
The Hebrew scriptures were written in Hebrew and as such needed interpretation (Aramaic being the common language of first century Palestine) by an Amora, who would interpret as the reader read from the scriptures. Sometimes, the Amora commented on difficult verses.

Temple, the
The Temple was the national centre of worship for the Hebrews. It was the

seat of the presence of God on earth. The magnificent Temple of Solomon had been destroyed in 587 BC by Babylonian power, but rebuilt during the reign of Cyrus (538 BC). By 19 BC, Herod the Great had begun rebuilding the Temple, restoring it to its former magnificence.

Tetrarch
Four tetrarchs would lead an ethnic group or province in the 1st century BC Near East, within the Roman Empire. All tetrarchs were subordinate to an ethnarch.

Tiberius, Emperor
Known as Tiberius Caesar Augustus or Tiberius I, he reigned as tyrannical Roman Emperor from 14 AD to 37 AD after a distinguished military career.

Torah, the
The written law, otherwise known as the Mosaic law. The first five books of the Hebrew bible comprise the Torah. It is distinct from the oral law, which is called the Mishnah.

Yeshua
The original Aramaic proper name for Jesus. A common name during the era of the second Temple, it is translated 'salvation'.

Yom Kippur
This is the holiest day of the Jewish year, the Day of Atonement, and is usually celebrated with a 24-hour period of fasting and prayer. According to the Hebrew calendar, it is performed on the 10th day of the 7th month.